Odd Streak

Discovered

TONY LOPES

ℛ
RAVETTE PUBLISHING

THE ODD STREAK © 2004 Tony Lopes.
All rights reserved.

Licensed by PSL.

This edition first published by Ravette Publishing 2004.

Printed and bound in Malta for
Ravette Publishing Limited
Unit 3, Tristar Centre
Star Road, Partridge Green
West Sussex RH13 8RA

ISBN: 1 84161 223 5

for Mum, thank you

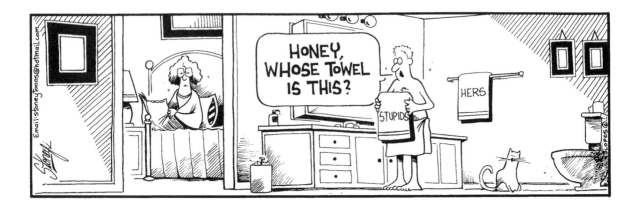

THE FIRST
BRAINSTORM

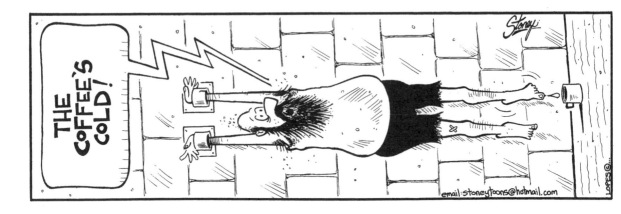